So This is Me

So this is me...I'm a tad wacky and just shy of crazy.

And I love to create. Whether I'm painting fine art in my studio, drawing my wacky characters on location at shows, sitting at my pottery wheel on my back porch, or writing at my computer, the creative process is liberating beyond words. I am forever exploring new ways to express the energy inside me. But I feel forever blessed to have these gifts and vow to never take them for granted.

I'm 50-something years old and live mere feet from the ocean in a funky little surf town called New Smyrna Beach, Florida. Yes, I know. New Smyrna Beach has been officially declared the "Shark Bite Capital of the World," but the sand sparkles like white crystals and the water is a thousand shades of aqua blue. Waking up every morning to this glorious sight makes my heart tingle. I share that space with my husband, Al, and a goofy Labrador retriever named Lucy. I eat chocolate truffles while I paint—and when they run out, I quit. I drink Perrier sparkling water so often I'm considering taking out stock in the company. I practice yoga, which for some strange reason I think will help compensate for my horrible diet, and I sit on the beach with my toes in the sand every chance I get.

I have five grown children and fourteen grandkids who love me as much as I adore them. I've taught them to dip their French fries in their chocolate shakes, make up any words they want to any tune they like, and to never, ever color inside the lines. (However, they all feel the need to assure their friends that they also have another set of grandparents who are "normal.")

Here are some examples of my wacky characters and other
work that I have painted with my favorite medium, watercolors.

Add the Color...
Feel the Tingle

There's nothing more satisfying than finishing a work of art. It adds excitement and joy to your life. Or to use my favorite tag line, you "Feel the Tingle."

The fact is, not everyone likes to draw, but everybody loves to color. Thus, anyone can experience the joy of participating in creating a piece of art with a coloring book. That's the genius of the medium. It's fun, interesting, and very fulfilling.

It doesn't matter how creative you are, you can learn about color and finish a masterpiece worth displaying. That's the purpose of this introduction—to teach you this skill.

If you already know this stuff, have a ball. If you don't, this information is way worth the effort. It will influence the way you color your entire world, from your home to your clothing to your food. Yes, even how you apply your makeup. And you will become a coloring book guru to boot.

So let's begin.

Color Selection Is Critical

You definitely want that "wow" factor when you're finished. So you need to know which colors do and do not complement each other. Do it right, and it will look like a Picasso.

The most essential tool in color selection is the color wheel, presented to the right. Each color in the wheel is either PRIMARY, SECONDARY, or TERTIARY.

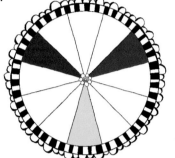

The primary colors are red, yellow, and blue. These are the root colors—they can't be created by mixing other colors. They are the pure foundation of the color wheel. All other colors are some combination of these three.

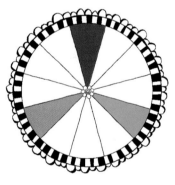

The secondary colors are orange, green, and purple. They are simply an equal mix of two primary colors (red + yellow = orange, yellow + blue = green, and blue + red = purple).

Tertiary colors are created by mixing a primary color with a secondary color. The resulting color is a matter of the percentage of the colors in the mix. There is no end to tertiary colors.

Colors are also categorized as warm or cool. Red, yellow, and orange are warm colors. Green, blue, and purple are cool colors. Selecting warm or cool colors really sets the mood of your piece. Warm colors are bold and exciting, while cool colors are more calm and peaceful.

Things really get interesting when you start playing with variations of a color. You can "tint" a color by adding white to the mix. Or you can "shade" a color by adding black.

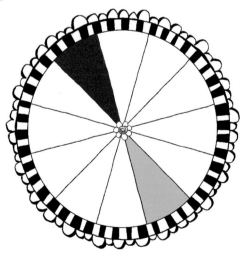

Colors opposite each other on the color wheel are called "complementary" and really pop off the page when they are used adjacent to each other. That's why you see yellow writing on purple backgrounds on billboards all over town. Or vice versa.

My Personal Twist

Since my earliest days as an artist, I have embraced the color yellow. Whether I am painting in my preferred medium of watercolors or dabbling in acrylics, pencils, markers, inks, or crayons, I almost always start with a layer of pale yellow—especially on a piece I want to be on the warm side of the color wheel. This assures that any work of art gets a wash of sunshine, whether the final colors are green, yellow, orange, or red. It really makes the colors pop. Greens get limey, oranges get a tangerine glow, reds get fiery, and yellows get even more electric.

And don't forget to leave open spaces with no color for white. It's easy to want to color every single nook and cranny with one of your fun colors, but leaving enough white is just as important to give your finished piece a lovely balance.

This is how I add a unique touch that is totally me. You should experiment with your own ways to make the art feel uniquely you! You might do this with your color choices or by adding patterns and flourishes to the art (check out the open spaces at the top and bottom of each piece, perfect for patterning). Have fun playing around!

Celebrating the Sisterhood

Forever Friends, Color by Erica Avedikian

Embrace Your Enthusiasm, Color by Erica Avedikian

Rise by Lifting Others (Friendship), Color by Dawn Collins

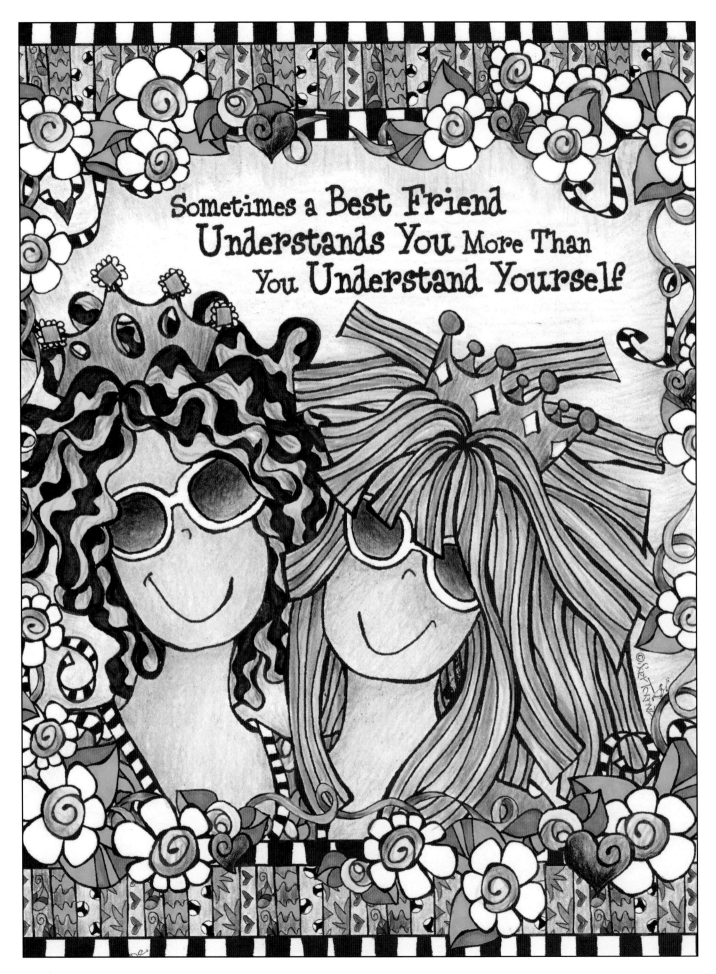

A Best Friend Understands, Color by Dawn Collins

Behind every successful woman is a substantial amount of chocolate

Amazing Memories, Color by Darla Tjelmeland

Long-Time Friends, Color by Erica Avedikian

Best Friends Are Sisters, Color by Erica Avedikian

Boots & Bling it's a COWGIRL THING!

Boots & Bling, Color by Erica Avedikian

Gathering of the Goddesses, Color by Suzy Toronto

Together, we are in the
presence of greatness.

_____
_____
_____
_____
_____
_____
_____
_____

Gathering of the Goddesses

Put On Some **Lipstick** and Go ROCK the **World**

©Suzy Toronto

Proclaim today as YOUR day
and this very instant to be your
moment for the taking.

Rock the World

We'll be friends forever, for always and no matter what

We've been through it all, but the challenges only drew us closer.

We'll Be Friends Forever

Rise by Lifting Others

Heart Air Balloon Rides NO CHARGE

The more you give, the more you get.

_____
_____
_____
_____
_____
_____
_____
_____

Rise by Lifting Others (Friendship)

good Times...
Wacky Friends...
Amazing
memories!

We are wonderful, wacky
women at their best.

_____
_____
_____
_____
_____
_____
_____
_____
_____

Amazing Memories

Embrace Your wild, wacky, over-the-top enthusiasm and don't let anyone tame you

Vow to forever surround yourself
with the wild energy that
makes your heart tingle.

_____
_____
_____
_____
_____
_____
_____
_____
_____
_____

Embrace Your Enthusiasm

Best Friends are the sisters we pick out ourselves!

We laugh when people ask if we're sisters—we're so much closer than that.

_____
_____
_____
_____
_____
_____
_____
_____
_____

Best Friends Are Sisters

Boots & Bling it's a Cowgirl thing!

Never underestimate the
power of glitter.

Boots & Bling

Remember what it felt like to giggle?
Now do it. Giggle!

_____
_____
_____
_____
_____
_____
_____
_____
_____

Silliness Makes Your Soul Smile

Behind every successful woman is a substantial amount of chocolate

Everyone should be actively
engaged in something they believe in.
I believe in chocolate.

Chocolate (Friendship)

We Are the Beach Babes

©Suzy Toronto

Life is just easier when you're
wearing flip-flops.

Beach Babes

...But I Like Being a Drama Queen!

Drama

Always wear your invisible crown.

_____
_____
_____
_____
_____
_____
_____
_____
_____
_____

Drama Queen (Friendship)

We didn't realize we were making memories, we just knew we were having fun.

If there is anything half as much fun
as living, I want to know what it is.

_____
_____
_____
_____
_____
_____
_____
_____
_____
_____

Making Memories

Don't let your frame of mind
frame you in.

_____
_____
_____
_____
_____
_____
_____
_____
_____
_____
_____

We used to be ordinary women. Now we are over-the-top, head-to-toe, honest-to-goodness legends!

_____
_____
_____
_____
_____
_____
_____
_____
_____

Live in the moment.

Flip-Flops

Anyone Who Says
She Doesn't Need a Girlfriend
Just Hasn't Found
a Good One Yet!

©Suzy Toronto

I will never find a friend as fun, crazy and wonderful as you...we are kindred spirits, soul mates forever.

_____

Girlfriend

Walk on the *edge* of your horizons and don't be afraid to sail over the edge.

_____

Footprints on the Moon

it's so **WONDERFUL** to have a **wacky friend like you**

©Suzy Toronto

Together we can let our wackiness
run wide and deep.

_____
_____
_____
_____
_____
_____
_____
_____
_____

Wacky Friend

You can't buy happiness, but... You Can Buy Cute Shoes... (and that's kinda the same thing)

All I want is peace on earth and
a really cute pair of shoes.

Buy Cute Shoes

How wonderful that I "get"
you and you "get" me.

_____
_____
_____
_____
_____
_____
_____
_____
_____
_____

A Best Friend Understands

I come "as is." No apologies.
No excuses. This is me!

_____
_____
_____
_____
_____
_____
_____
_____
_____

Pretending to Be Normal (Friendship)

We will be the two old ladies in the nursing home causing all the trouble...

I hope you know, I will always
be there for you.

Two Old Ladies

Play with wild abandon and
choose with no regret.

_____
_____
_____
_____
_____
_____
_____
_____
_____

Wanted: No Regrets

You know everything about me. All the
silly things that make me goofy...yet
you love me anyway.

_____

Your Kind of Wacky

Everyone makes mistakes—
you're in great company.

_____
_____
_____
_____
_____
_____
_____
_____
_____
_____

When You Stumble (Friendship)

I Believe in You.

I have always believed in you.
I think you are positively
over-the-top amazing
and don't ever
forget it!

Do you even have a clue about the
difference you have made in the
lives of everyone around you?

_____
_____
_____
_____
_____
_____
_____
_____
_____

Life Is All About How You Handle Plan B

Sometimes it's hard to tell the
difference between something trying
to kill you or making you stronger.

Plan B (Friendship)

Our friendship will stand
the test of time.

_____

Forever Friends

Don't let anyone dull your sparkle

©Suzy Toronto

Don't be afraid to be different and
stand out in a crowd. Be outstanding.

_____
_____
_____
_____
_____
_____
_____
_____
_____

Don't Let Anyone Dull Your Sparkle (Friendship)

Our friendship enjoys a depth
that only time can give.

Long-Time Friends

Together we laugh a **Little Louder**, smile a **Little Brighter** and live a **Little Better.**

©Suzy Toronto

Together, life is good—
better than good.

_____
_____
_____
_____
_____
_____
_____
_____
_____
_____

Together